Specific Skill Series

Drawing Conclusions

Richard A. Boning

Fifth Edition

SRA/McGraw-Hill

Columbus, Ohio

M000310917

SRA/McGraw-Hill

A Division of The **McGraw·Hill** *Companies*

Printed in the United States of America.

Send all inquiries to:
    SRA/McGraw-Hill
    250 Old Wilson Bridge Road, Suite 310
    Worthington, OH 43085

ISBN 0-02-687981-6

    5 6 7 8 9 IMP 00 99

To the Teacher

PURPOSE:

DRAWING CONCLUSIONS helps develop one of the most important interpretive skills. Pupils learn to look beyond the writer's literal statements to reach an unstated but logical conclusion based on those statements and sometimes their phrasing. In DRAWING CONCLUSIONS the correct conclusion is the most logical one for pupils to reach from only the information presented.

FOR WHOM:

The skill of DRAWING CONCLUSIONS is developed through a series of books spanning ten levels (Picture, Preparatory, A, B, C, D, E, F, G, H). The Picture Level is for pupils who have not acquired a basic sight vocabulary. The Preparatory Level is for pupils who have a basic sight vocabulary but are not yet ready for the first-grade-level book. Books A through H are appropriate for pupils who can read on levels one through eight, respectively. **The use of the *Specific Skill Series Placement Test* is recommended to determine the appropriate level.**

THE NEW EDITION:

The fifth edition of the *Specific Skill Series* maintains the quality and focus that has distinguished this program for more than 25 years. A key element central to the program's success has been the unique nature of the reading selections. Nonfiction pieces about current topics have been designed to stimulate the interest of students, motivating them to use the comprehension strategies they have learned to further their reading. To keep this important aspect of the program intact, a percentage of the reading selections have been replaced in order to ensure the continued relevance of the subject material.

In addition, a significant percentage of the artwork in the program has been replaced to give the books a contemporary look. The cover photographs are designed to appeal to readers of all ages.

SESSIONS:

Short practice sessions are the most effective. It is desirable to have a practice session every day or every other day, using a few units each session.

To the Teacher

SCORING:

Pupils should record their answers on the reproducible worksheets. The worksheets make scoring easier and provide uniform records of the pupils' work. Using worksheets also avoids consuming the exercise books.

It is important for pupils to know how well they are doing. For this reason, units should be scored as soon as they have been completed. Then a discussion can be held in which pupils justify their choices. (The Integrated Language Activities, many of which are open-ended, do not lend themselves to an objective score; thus there are no answer keys for these pages.)

GENERAL INFORMATION ON *DRAWING CONCLUSIONS*:

The questions in DRAWING CONCLUSIONS do not deal with direct references; thus the answers do not use the same words as the paragraphs. On the Picture Level, the readers examine the picture for the correct answer. The Preparatory, A, and B levels contain primarily indirect references; that is, the answers are found in the paragraphs but with slightly different wording. Some easy conclusions are also included. As the books advance in challenge, there are more difficult conclusions, involving less obvious relationships. The conclusions also become more dependent on qualifying words such as "mostly," "all," "some," or "only."

In DRAWING CONCLUSIONS the readers are asked to find an example, note a contrast, generalize, see cause and effect relationships, detect a mood, see an analogy, identify a time or place relationship, make a comparison, or anticipate an outcome.

It is important that the teacher ask pupils to find in the paragraph the specific information relevant to the tentative conclusion. Then pupils must test the conclusion against the information provided. When the emphasis is placed on finding evidence to prove answers and when the pupils put themselves in roles of detectives, not only does their ability to draw conclusions rapidly improve, but they also have fun.

Pupils must know that a conclusion is a judgment made. It must be supported by strong evidence. In DRAWING CONCLUSIONS the correct answer is one that is either highly likely or certain.

Some alternate answer choices may be true. The answer that is accepted as correct, however, must not only be true but must have supportive evidence in the paragraph. The clue may hinge on a single word, involve a phrase or a sentence, or encompass the paragraph as a whole.

RELATED MATERIALS:

Specific Skill Series Placement Tests, which enable the teacher to place pupils at their appropriate levels in each skill, are available for the Elementary (Pre-1–6) and Midway (4–8) grade levels.

About This Book

A writer does not tell you everything in a story. Sometimes you need to figure out things that are not told. This is called **drawing a conclusion**. A conclusion is what you can tell from what the writer tells you.

Good readers draw conclusions as they read. They use what the writer tells them. Drawing a conclusion is like answering a riddle. Read this riddle. Think about the clues it gives. Can you tell what this thing is?

I have a face and hands. I often hang on a wall. I can tell you the time of day.

Did you guess that this is a clock? You can draw that conclusion from clues in the riddle.

In this book, you will read stories. For each story, choose the answer that tells what you can tell from the story. Remember to use clues in the story to draw a conclusion.

Fish make good pets. They need clean water and something to eat. Fish swim up and down and around. They never stop. It's fun to see them eat and play.

From the story you can tell that—

  (A) **pet fish are often blue**
  (B) **people eat with their pet fish**
  (C) **fish keep moving**

Our car is lost. Where can it be? We look and look. We can't find our new red car. There it is. It's on the other side of that big blue bus.

From the story you can tell that—

    (A) a big bus can hide a car

    (B) the bus took the car's place

    (C) red cars can go fast

Tom went to the dog race. A rabbit was in front of the dogs. "Oh, no!" said Tom. "Will they catch it?"

"It's all right," said Father. "It's only a toy rabbit."

From the story you can tell that—

   (A) Father told Tom something the dogs did not know

   (B) the dogs did not want to catch the rabbit

   (C) Tom would like to see the dogs catch the rabbit

The cat was after the bird. Then another bird came to help its friend. Soon another bird came. Now they were all after the cat. The cat ran away!

From the story you can tell that—

(A) **the cat began the fight**
(B) **the birds began the fight**
(C) **the cat did not run away**

The children had a turtle race. One turtle was in front. Then it stopped. The children began to laugh. What a surprise! The turtle had gone to sleep.

From the story you can tell that—

(A) one turtle was tired
(B) the children did not think that the race was funny
(C) turtles sleep all day

The house behind Ann's house was on fire! Ann ran to tell Father and Mother. Soon the firefighters came. They put out the fire. "Thanks, Ann," they said. "You did the right thing."

From the story you can tell that—

(A) Ann tried to put out the fire

(B) Mother and Father ran away

(C) Mother and Father called the firefighters

A cow was in the road. It would not move. Then a farmer came. The farmer took the cow away. "Thanks," said the people in the cars. "We could have been here all day!"

From the story you can tell that—

(A) the farmer helped the people

(B) the cow did not go away

(C) the cow got into a truck

"Look at this!" cried Dot. "Did you ever see a green dog?" Mother came to look. What was it? Then they saw. It was Nip! The baby had put green paint on the dog!

From the story you can tell that—

(A) Mother was first to see the dog

(B) Mother would like to see another color

(C) Dot saw the dog first

Bill went by the monkey cage. "Where did my hat go?" asked Bill. Then his friends began to laugh. Soon Bill began to laugh, too. The monkey had his hat. The hat was on the monkey's head!

From the story you can tell that—

(A) **Bill thought the monkey was funny**

(B) **the monkey gave the hat back to Bill**

(C) **the monkey began to eat the hat**

"Can we give something to Tom, the cat?" asked Rosa. "It's his birthday." Mother went to get something. Would it be a cake? She came back. She had a fish! Tom had a happy birthday.

From the story you can tell that—

(A) **Tom liked fish**

(B) **Rosa did not have a good time**

(C) **Rosa got a cake, too**

The children began to play catch. Then a big dog came. Bob and Tom began to run. Maria did not run. "Come back," said Maria. "I know this dog. It just wants to make friends."

From the story you can tell that—

    (A) Maria had seen the dog before

    (B) Bob and Tom knew the dog

    (C) the dog did not like Bob and Tom

At the zoo the baby elephant cried each night. The other animals could not sleep. One night the zookeeper put on a night-light. It gave just a little light. The baby elephant stopped crying and went to sleep.

From the story you can tell that—

    (A) the zookeeper ran out of food

    (B) the other animals did not like to sleep

    (C) the baby elephant was afraid of the dark

At the zoo the baby elephant cried each night. The other animals could not sleep. One night the zookeeper put on a night-light. It gave just a little light. The baby elephant stopped crying and went to sleep.

A. Exercising Your Skill

Read the story above. Think about what the story says. On your paper, answer these questions.

1. Where does the story take place?
2. What was the baby elephant doing?
3. Why couldn't the other animals sleep?
4. Why did the zookeeper put on a night-light?
5. Why did the baby elephant go to sleep at last?

B. Expanding Your Skill

Talk about the questions in Part A. Which answers were given in the story? Which answers did you have to figure out? How did you figure out the answers?

C. Exploring Language

Tell the story of the baby elephant. Write a word on your paper for each blank. Spell the best you can.

The baby elephant _____ each night. The other elephants could not sleep because of the _____ . One night the _____ put on a night-light. It worked! The baby elephant went right to _____ !

Now write a name for the story.

D. Expressing Yourself

Do one of these things.

1. Write a story about a baby animal. Give your story a good ending.

2. Act out the story in Part A. Work with two or more of your classmates.

3. Draw a picture about the story in Part A. Then talk about the picture you drew.

Would you like to have a pet pig? A man in the South has one. The man brings the pig to work. They are good friends. People come from all over to see the man's pet.

From the story you can tell that—

    (A) there are many pet pigs

    (B) no one looks at a pet pig

    (C) the pig and the man like each other

"Don't walk in the boat," said Father. But Ann began to walk. She fell into the water. Father got her back into the boat.

"From now on I'll do as you say," said Ann.

___

From the story you can tell that—

(A) **Ann did what Father told her**

(B) **Ann did not do what Father told her**

(C) **Father could not get Ann back into the boat**

Bam! Bam! What were those sounds? The children ran to see. It was just the baby. Pans and spoons were all around. The baby was having fun playing with them.

From the story you can tell that—

    (A) the children were in no hurry

    (B) the children took the pans away

    (C) the baby was playing

Peg saw a little rabbit. "It will make a good pet," she said. "I will catch it." She ran and ran, but she could not catch the rabbit. "Maybe I can buy another pet at the pet store," she said.

From the story you can tell that—

(A) **Peg wanted a pet**
(B) **Peg caught the rabbit**
(C) **the rabbit was not as fast as Peg**

The children were playing under a big tree on the farm. "Look out," cried Jan. "There are bees in this tree. They have made their home here." The children quickly ran to another part of the farm.

From the story you can tell that—

    (A) the children did not want to get hurt

    (B) the children wanted to get honey

    (C) the children were not afraid

It's fun to paint a picture. All you need is something nice to look at. Maybe you will want to paint a picture of some rocks by the water.

From the story you can tell that—

(A) no one will paint rocks by the water
(B) you can paint what you like to see
(C) you cannot paint a picture of an animal

"You should not fish there," said Peg.

"Why?" asked Dot.

Then a big cow came. It ran after Dot. Dot ran. She got away. "Now I know why!" said Dot.

From the story you can tell that—

    (A) there were no fish there

    (B) the cow would run after the fish

    (C) this was not a good place to fish

A fox was after a rabbit. The rabbit went down into its home. It came up behind the fox. The fox didn't see it. The rabbit got away.

From the story you can tell that—

   (A) in one way a rabbit's home is like ours
   (B) the rabbit could not find its home
   (C) the fox did not get the rabbit

The children had some bread. They went to give it to the ducks. The ducks were happy. The bread was good! The children were happy, too. "This is fun," they said.

From the story you can tell that—

(A) the children were ready to catch the ducks

(B) the children had a good time

(C) the ducks did not eat

A fox was after the chickens. They could not get away. Soon it would eat them. Who could help them? Then along came Rags. Rags began to bark. The fox ran away.

From the story you can tell that—

    (A) the chickens had a good time

    (B) the fox did not eat the chickens

    (C) the fox ran after Rags

It was a big fish! Could Rosa bring it in? It was a long fight, but she did it. People came to take her picture. The fish was as big as Rosa!

From the story you can tell that—

    (A) Rosa had a lot of help

    (B) people did not think much of the fish

    (C) it was not easy to catch the fish

We take a bird walk. We see many kinds of birds. We hear them sing. We walk near a tree where some birds live. The father and mother birds are giving their little ones something to eat.

From the story you can tell that—

    (A) a bird walk shows us how birds live

    (B) birds like to walk and talk all day

    (C) little birds don't eat very much

The children were playing under a big tree on the farm. "Look out," cried Jan. "There are bees in this tree. They have made their home here." The children quickly ran to another part of the farm.

A. Exercising Your Skill

Read the story. Think about what it says. On your paper, draw the boxes below. Then fill in the answers to the questions.

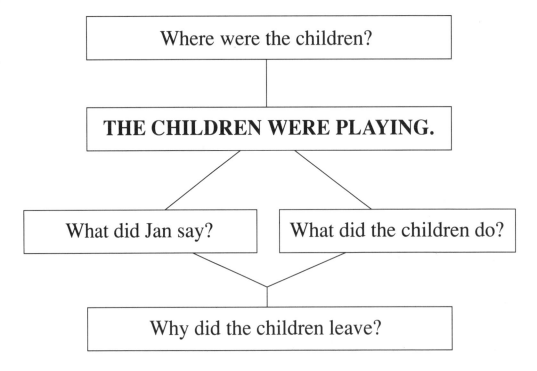

B. Expanding Your Skill

Talk about the story. Does the story tell you why the children ran away quickly? What clues in the story can you use to figure it out?

C. Exploring Language

Think about these stories. Answer each question.

1.   Jim and Ann were sitting at the table. They were watching TV. Jim looked at the clock. "Oh, no," he said. "We need to do our homework. Mom will be home from work soon. She told us what we had to do before we watched TV."

   Did Ann and Jim do what their mother wanted them to?
   How can you tell?

2.   "Dad," Jim said. "I washed the dog. I cleaned my room. I put away the dishes. I did just what you said to do. May I go outside and play ball now?"

   Did Jim do what his father wanted him to?
   How can you tell?

D. Expressing Yourself

Do one of these things.

1. Think about something you like to do outdoors at a certain time of year. Tell your class about it. Do not tell them what time of year you are thinking of, but give clues. See if your class can tell what time of year you are thinking of.

2. In a magazine find a picture that shows a person. Show the picture to your class. Tell what you think the person is thinking or saying. Use clues in the picture to figure it out.

Sam saw a baby bear. He began to play with it. Mother stopped him. "Don't play with the baby bear," said Mother. "The mother bear is never far away. Let's go before she gets back."

From the story you can tell that—

- **(A) the baby bear is lost**
- **(B) Sam is lost**
- **(C) the mother bear will come soon**

Peg was out on a farm. She had never been away from town. "Look, Tom," said Peg. "There is a baby horse."

"No," said Tom, "that is my pony. We can ride it."

From the story you can tell that—

(A) **Tom had never been on a farm**

(B) **Peg had never seen a pony**

(C) **the pony had never been on a farm**

Les was out in front. It was the last jump. Would her horse make it? There was no time to think. Up, up, and over went the horse. Les came in first!

From the story you can tell that—

(A) **there is another jump to go**

(B) **Les was behind**

(C) **no one could catch Les**

Tom and Father went into a little house. It was way out on the ice. They began to fish. Tom got one! It was the first fish of the day. It was a big one.

From the story you can tell that—

(A) the house was made of ice

(B) Father was cold

(C) Father did not make the first catch

"Come see our two rabbits," said Maria.

"You don't have two rabbits anymore," said Ann. "Look in the cage!" There were six rabbits. There were four new baby rabbits!

From the story you can tell that—

- **(A) Maria did not know how many rabbits she had**
- (B) there were three new rabbits
- (C) the new rabbits were no surprise

Peg put the big fish into the water. She put it in with the little fish. When she came back, the little fish was gone.

"It is not good to do that," said Rosa. "Big fish eat little fish."

From the story you can tell that—

(A) **Rosa knew where the little fish went**
(B) **Peg knew a lot about fish**
(C) **the big fish did not know where the little fish went**

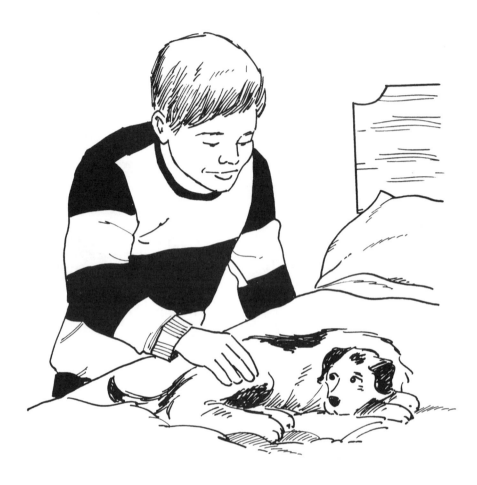

Bob went to get his coat. It was on the bed. He put his hand on something. Was it his coat? It was too dark to see. Then the "something" went "Bow wow!" It was Nip.

From the story you can tell that—

    (A) the room was green

    (B) the dog was under the coat

    (C) Bob could not see very well

The children saw a fox. "I wish our friends were here," said Ron. "They will say that we didn't see it."

"No," said Lee, "I'll take a picture. Then they will know that we saw it!"

From the story you can tell that—

    (A) not many people see a fox outside of the zoo

    (B) the fox ran away

    (C) Ron did not see the fox

The lights went out. No one could see. "What can we do?" asked Jan.

Mother went over to a box. She did something to it. The lights went on. "Now we can see," said Mother.

From the story you can tell that—

(A) **Mother knew what was wrong**

(B) **the lights went off again**

(C) **Jan made the lights go on**

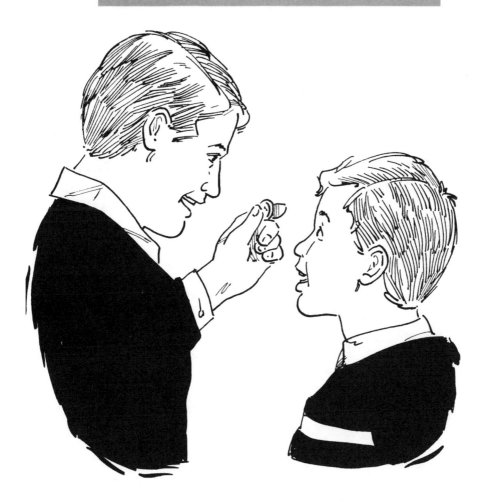

Tom found an old penny. He took it to Father.

"It's a good thing you let me see it," said Father. "This penny is very old. You can get a lot of money for it."

From the story you can tell that—

    (A) Father had lost the penny

    (B) Tom dropped the penny

    (C) the penny was not new

The dog saw its own face in the water. It thought another dog was there. It began to bark. Ann began to laugh. "You funny dog," said Ann. "That's your own face!"

From the story you can tell that—

    (A) the dog did not like the water

    (B) the dog did not know who the dog in the water was

    (C) the dog did not look like the dog in the water

The duck could not fly. What would happen? Sam took it into the house. Soon it got well. One day the duck flew up into the air. It went off with the other ducks. Sam was happy.

From the story you can tell that—

    (A) the duck did not get well

    (B) Sam made a house for the duck

    (C) Sam was glad to see the duck fly

Ramon was in bed. He saw Marta. She was up. "Why are you up?" asked Ramon. Marta didn't say a word. She was walking in her sleep.

From the story you can tell that—

   (A) Ramon could not find Marta

   (B) Marta could not find Ramon

   (C) Marta could not hear Ramon

"May I have a balloon, Father?" asked Peg.

"Yes," said Father. "What color do you want?"

"Red," said Peg. Father gave the man some money. Peg got her red balloon!

From the story you can tell that—

(A) **Peg did not want a balloon**

(B) **Peg did not want a red balloon**

(C) **all the balloons were not red**

Peg put the big fish into the water. She put it in with the little fish. When she came back, the little fish was gone.

"It is not good to do that," said Rosa. "Big fish eat little fish."

A. Exercising Your Skill

Read the story. Think about what it tells you. On your paper, answer these questions.

1. What did Peg put into the water?
2. What was in the water already?
3. When Peg came back to look, how many fish were in the water?
4. What did Rosa say wasn't good to do?
5. What happened to the little fish?

B. Expanding Your Skill

Read these sentences. They tell about the story. One thing does not belong. On your paper, write the three sentences that tell what happened.

Peg had a big fish.
Peg put it in the water with the little fish.
The two fish became friends.
The big fish ate the little one.

What clues in the story helped you figure out what happened?

C. Exploring Language

What animal does each group of sentences tell about? Write the name on your paper. Spell the name the best you can.

1.   I live in a large bowl of water. The children look at me. Each day one child gets to feed me. I'm bright orange, and I love to swim all day.

   I am a _____ .

2.   I live in a nice warm house and sleep on a child's bed at night. I have four legs and a tail. My owner shouts at me when I bark or jump up on people. When I'm good, I get a bone!

   I am a _____ .

3.   I live in a zoo. I'm a tall animal with a very long neck. I love to eat snacks from the tops of trees.

   I am a _____ .

D. Expressing Yourself

In a small group, play "Who Am I?" Tell about an animal. Do not name it. See if your friends can name the animal.

The cat saw a balloon. It began to play with the balloon. The cat began to play too hard! Bam! Where was the balloon? It was gone. The cat didn't know what to think.

From the story you can tell that—

(A) the cat did not know what it had done

(B) the cat was ready to eat the balloon

(C) the cat got another balloon

The children found a cage. "What will we put in it?" they asked. "It's too big for a fly. It's too small for a deer."

"It's just right for this little red hen," said Joe.

From the story you can tell that—

　　(A)　the cage was very big
　　(B)　the deer was too small
　　(C)　the hen was put in the cage

"Let's sing something," said Ron. The children began to sing. Then they stopped. There were funny sounds! What were they?

Then Jan said, "It's just Tip. Tip likes to sing, too!"

From the story you can tell that—

    (A) Tip does not like to sing

    (B) Tip does not like the children to sing

    (C) at first the children did not know that Tip was singing, too

"Coach made us swim a mile today," said Pat and Lee. "Swimming makes us hungry."

"You two need to swim well," said Jan and Les. "We will cheer for you at the meet tomorrow."

From the story you can tell that—

    (A) **Pat and Lee are on the swim team**

    (B) **Jan and Les don't like food**

    (C) **Pat and Lee can't swim**

"I don't have a horse," said Bob. "I will ride the goat." He got on the goat. The goat just sat down.

Ann saw them. She began to laugh. "You have a funny horse!" said Ann.

From the story you can tell that—

    (A) the goat did not make a good horse

    (B) Bob never rode a horse

    (C) the goat made a good horse

The birds made their home. They made it by the window. Jan saw them. What was the home for? Then one day she found out. There were baby birds in it!

From the story you can tell that—

(A) the baby birds did not surprise Jan

(B) Jan did not see the birds build the home

(C) the baby birds did not build the home

Pat was lost in the dark. His feet went down. His shoes got wet. Pat said, "I am near the pond. I will go up where it is dry. I can see the lights of my house up there."

From the story you can tell that—

(A) **Pat wanted to fish**
(B) **Pat found out where he was**
(C) **Pat ran for help**

The children saw a bear in a cage. A man was in the cage with it. The man had the bear sit up. Then he had it ride a bike. "I didn't know bears could do that!" said the children.

From the story you can tell that—

(A) the children found out some things bears can do

(B) the children found out what bears cannot do

(C) the children found out how bears eat

The man took a look at all the pigs. Then he saw Dot's pig. It was a big one. "Your pig is better than the others," said the man. "You win first prize!"

From the story you can tell that—

(A) Dot lost her pig
(B) Dot did not really own the pig
(C) the man had seen other pigs

Bob found a toy truck. It was still good, but it was old. "Maybe we can make it look new," said Father. Father got some paint. Soon the truck did look like new. Bob was happy.

From the story you can tell that—

(A) the truck was new
(B) Father made it look old
(C) something old can be made to look new

Peg could not find Tip. "The dog must be lost!" said Peg. She went to her room to cry. There was a sound under her bed. It was Tip. The dog had been there all the time!

From the story you can tell that—

(A) **Peg was sad when she couldn't find Tip**
(B) **Mother saw Tip**
(C) **Peg and Tip were lost**

Mrs. Parks came to visit the class. She told a very funny story. The children laughed and laughed. Then they picked some flowers for Mrs. Parks. "Thank you for the funny story," the children said.

From the story you can tell that—

(A) the boys and girls liked the story

(B) Mrs. Parks did not like the children

(C) the story was sad

Pat was lost in the dark. His feet went down. His shoes got wet. Pat said, "I am near the pond. I will go up where it is dry. I can see the lights of my house up there."

A. Exercising Your Skill

Read the story above. On your paper, complete the story map. Tell what Pat did in the story. In the boxes, write the answers to the questions.

PAT WAS LOST.

What Did Pat Do?
1. _____
2. _____
3. _____

PAT WAS NOT LOST.

B. Expanding Your Skill

Talk about the story.

1. Did Pat know where he was?
2. What happened to his feet?
3. How did Pat know he was near the pond?
4. What did Pat think to do?
5. Why was he happy to see the lights of his house?

C. Exploring Language

Think about the following places you could be. On your paper, write what places the sentences are talking about. Spell the best you can.

1.   You are hot. The sun is shining. You cannot wait to jump into the water.

    Where are you? _____

2.   You put the food into the cart. You get in line. You get out your money.

    Where are you? _____

D. Expressing Yourself

Do one of these things.

1. Read the story in Part A again. Write a new ending for the story. Draw a picture to go with the story.

2. Have you ever been scared? Write a story about a scary thing that happened. The story can be made up, or it can be real.

3. Pretend you are Pat. Tell your class what you did and how you felt the night you got lost.